MEDIC #1

LATLINE

UBLE TAKE

D1515070

$2.50

JEMAS | ROWE | FINKELSTEIN | SOVIERO | CASTIELLO

THEN

NOW

	1966	2015
WORLD POPULATION	3,400,000,000	7,200,000,000
McDonald's		
LOCATIONS	850	36,000
COUNTRIES	1	118
BIGGEST BURGER	1.6oz	5.4oz
AVERAGE MEAL CALORIES	590	1,500
Walmart		
LOCATIONS	24	11,495
COUNTRIES	1	28
PERCENTAGE OF PRODUCTS MADE IN CHINA	0%	70%
NFL		
SUPER BOWL VIEWERS	50,000,000	114,000,000
AVERAGE SALARY	$15,000	$1,900,000
Apple		
LOCATIONS	0	453
iOS DEVICES SOLD	0	1,000,000,000
Prison Industry		
STATE AND FEDERAL PRISON POPULATION	200,000	2,300,000
PERCENTAGE OF FEDERAL PRISON POPULATION: DRUG VIOLATIONS	11%–16%	50%
Health Industry		
COST OF HEALTH CARE	$201 PER CAPITA	$10,000 PER CAPITA
COST OF MEDICARE	$3,000,000,000	$634,300,000,000
Political Industry		
COST OF PRESIDENTIAL CAMPAIGN	$8,800,000	$5,000,000,000

STORY
BILL JEMAS
BRIAN FINKELSTEIN

SCRIPT
BRIAN FINKELSTEIN
MIKE SOVIERO
MICHAEL COAST

LAYOUTS
JULIAN ROWE

PENCILS
MARCO CASTIELLO

COLORS
THOMAS CHU

COVER
APPLE QINGYANG ZHANG

LETTERS
DAVE LANPHEAR
RICHARD BROOKS

EDITOR
RICHARD BROOKS

RICHARD BROOKS | PRODUCTION ASSISTANT

MICHAEL COAST | STORY EDITOR

CLAIRE DRANGINIS | PRODUCTION COORDINATOR

CAROLINE FLANAGAN | PRODUCTION ASSISTANT

ALLISON GADSDEN | EDITORIAL INTERN

WILLIAM GRAVES | DIGITAL PRODUCTION ARTIST

CHARLOTTE GREENBAUM | EDITORIAL ASSISTANT

YOUNG HELLER | STORYBOARD ILLUSTRATOR

BILL JEMAS | GENERAL MANAGER

ELYSIA LIANG | EDITORIAL ASSISTANT

ROBERT MEYERS | MANAGING EDITOR

JULIAN ROWE | STORYBOARD ILLUSTRATOR

LILLIAN TAN | BUSINESS MANAGER

GABE YOCUM | SALES & MARKETING COORDINATOR

Coming up: Information on the Venus Probe...

We're coming in with a 27-year-old male with severe chest injuries, over.

...shot down by NASA last night...

Any head or neck trauma?

...due to high levels of radiation.

Nothing's visible, but he's unconscious.

We've also got a 28-year-old woman, severe lacerations on her head. Delirious and possible concussion. Over.

HELLO?!? You all forgetting something?

EMERGENCY

We'll be right with you, sir.

Better be!

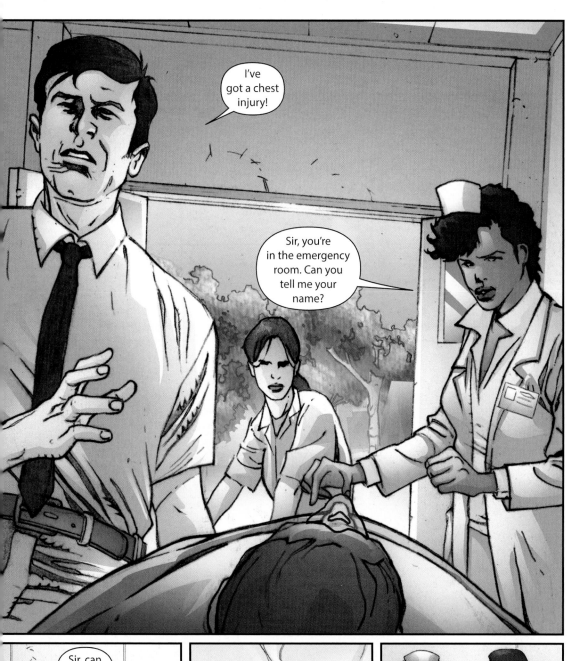

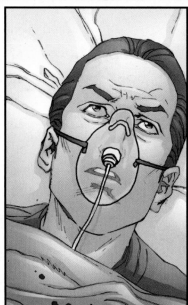

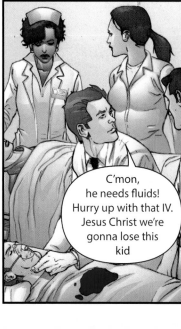

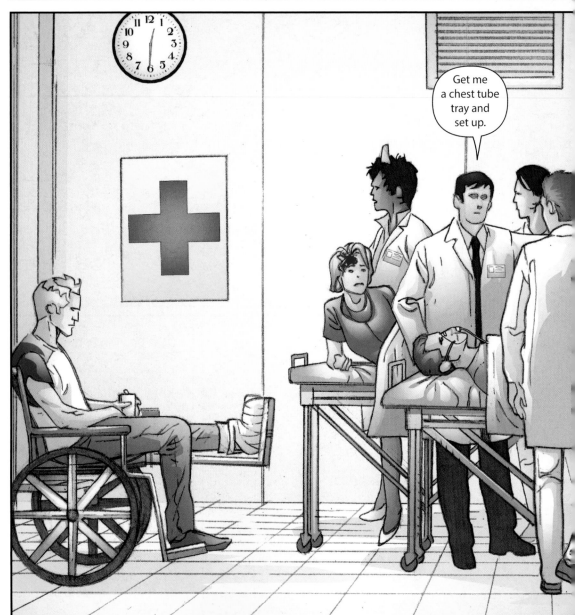

Is my husband okay?

Ma'am, we're taking your husband into surgery now.

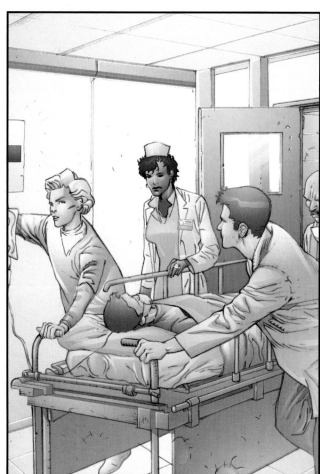

But he's in good hands. Dr. Bricker is one of the best surgeons in the state.

I was a very late bloomer when it came to girls.

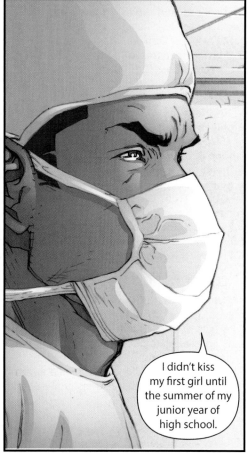

I didn't kiss my first girl until the summer of my junior year of high school.

Can you survive the zombie apocalypse?

Yes? You probably think you can.

There is only one way to find out.

Play the **Dead Reign® RPG**. The core rule book, a few players, some dice and an active imagination are all you need to start playing. Rules are easy. Character creation is fast and fun. Combat, quick and deadly. Survival? Harder than you may think.

● **7 different types of zombies. Zombie combat and survival tips.**

● **6 Apocalyptic Character Classes and Ordinary People.**

● **101 Random Scenarios, Encounters, Settings and places of note.**

● **100 Random Corpse Searches, other tables, weapons & vehicles.**

● **Death Cults, their Priests, power over zombies and goals.**

● **Quick Roll Character Creation tables (10 minutes).**

● **5 sourcebooks provide more types of zombies, survival tips, new dangers and adventure.**

● **The Dead Reign™ core rule book is 224 pages – Cat. No. 230. A complete role-playing game book.**

Discover the Palladium Books® RPG Megaverse®

Fun to read. A blast to play. The Palladium role-playing rule system is the same in every game. This means once readers become familiar with one game, they can play them *ALL*.

Better yet, you can link and combine several game worlds to create epic, multi-dimensional adventures on a cosmic scale!

What's that? You've never seen a role-playing game? The role-playing core rule book contains all rules and data you need to create characters and get you started. Each game or supplement is a magazine size soft-bound or hardcover book, 48-352 pages, and jam-packed with great art, heroes, villains, adventures and tons of ideas. **Dead Reign®** and **Robotech®** are excellent for those of you new to pen and paper RPGs.

Rifts® is the Earth of the future, but a transformed and alien Earth where magic and technology coexist and realities from countless dimensions collide. Alien predators and supernatural monsters prey upon human survivors and threaten to conquer the world.

Players can be any number of aliens, mutants, warriors, cyborgs, robots and wizards. Lines of magic crisscross the Earth, giving life to dragons, godlings and supernatural horrors. They also lead to dimensional gateways called "Rifts" that link the Earth to the infinite Megaverse®. In **Rifts®** anything is possible.

Unleash your imagination! Drop by our website, learn more about our games or make purchases from our online store. Also available in comic book and game stores everywhere.

www.palladiumbooks.com

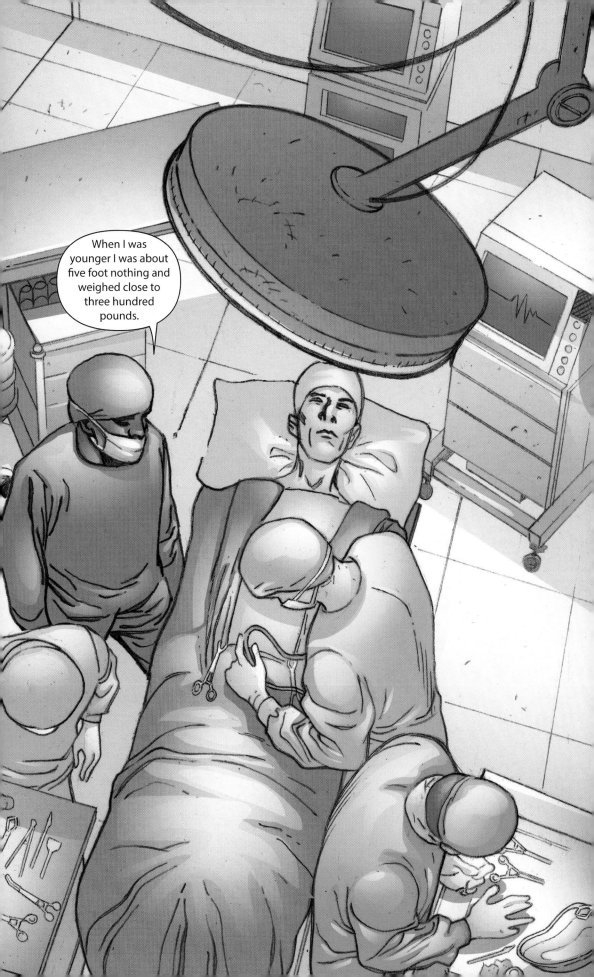

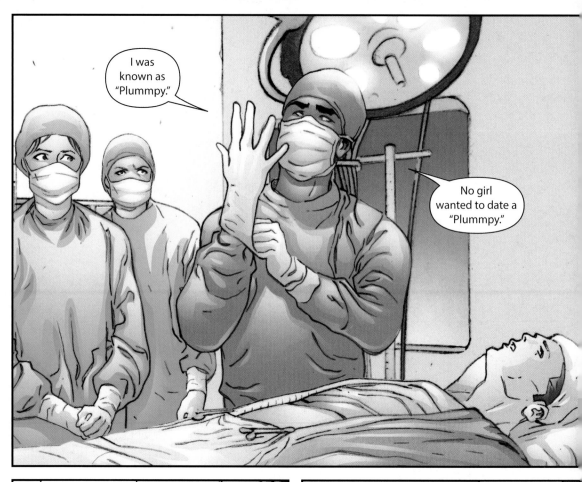

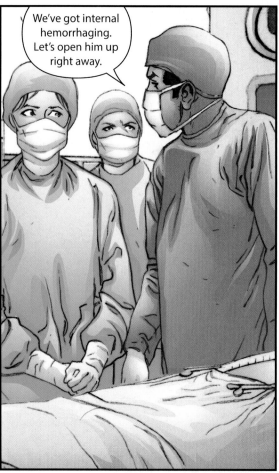

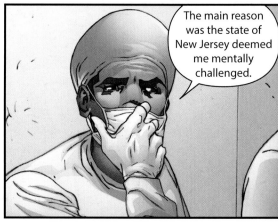

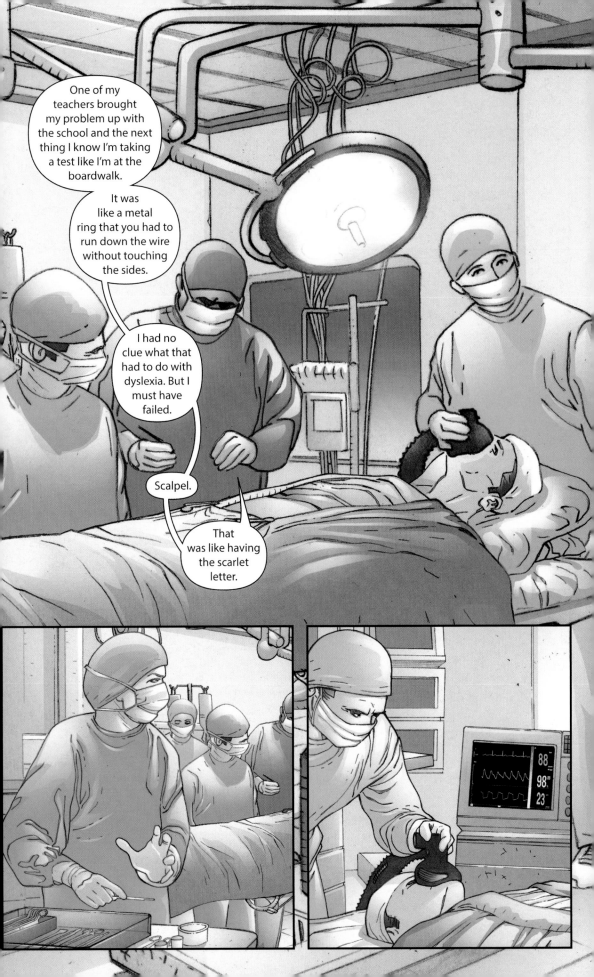

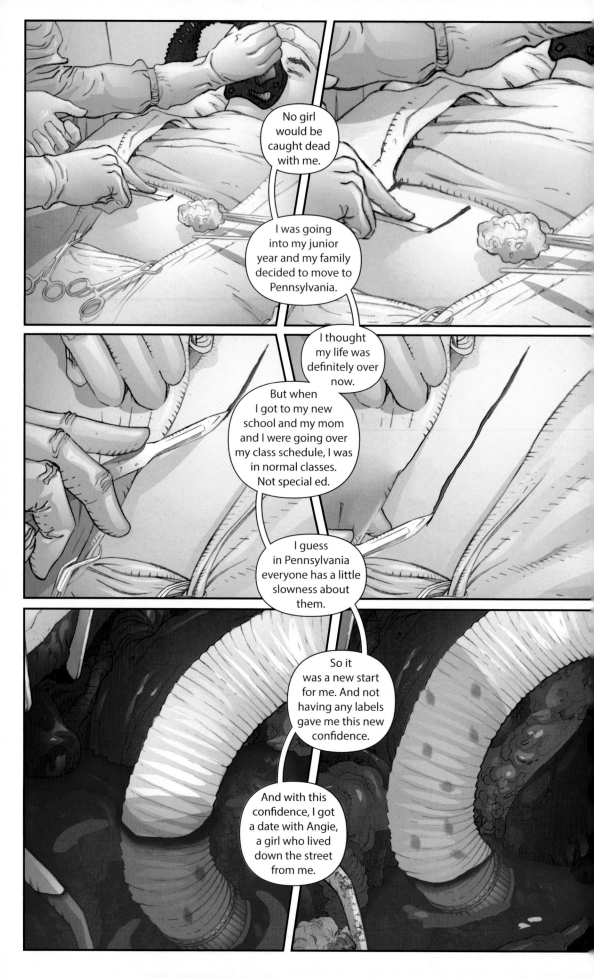

DISCOVER THE LARGEST INDEPENDENT SUPERHERO UNIVERSE
IN COMICS | EACH VOLUME ONE ONLY $9.99

THE VALIANT

X-O MANOWAR
VOL. 1: BY THE SWORD

BLOODSHOT REBORN
VOL. 1: COLORADO

HARBINGER
VOL. 1: OMEGA RISING

DIVINITY

QUANTUM AND WOODY
VOL. 1: THE WORLD'S WORST
SUPERHERO TEAM

THE DEATH-DEFYING
DR. MIRAGE

RAI
VOL. 1: WELCOME TO NEW JAPAN

NINJAK
VOL. 1: WEAPONEER

ARCHER & ARMSTRONG
VOL. 1: THE MICHELANGELO CODE

IVAR, TIMEWALKER
VOL. 1: MAKING HISTORY

IMPERIUM
VOL. 1: COLLECTING MONSTERS

SID MEIER'S CIVILIZATION®
BEYOND EARTH™

WWW.CIVILIZATION.COM

EVERYONE 10+

Alcohol Reference
Fantasy Violence
Language

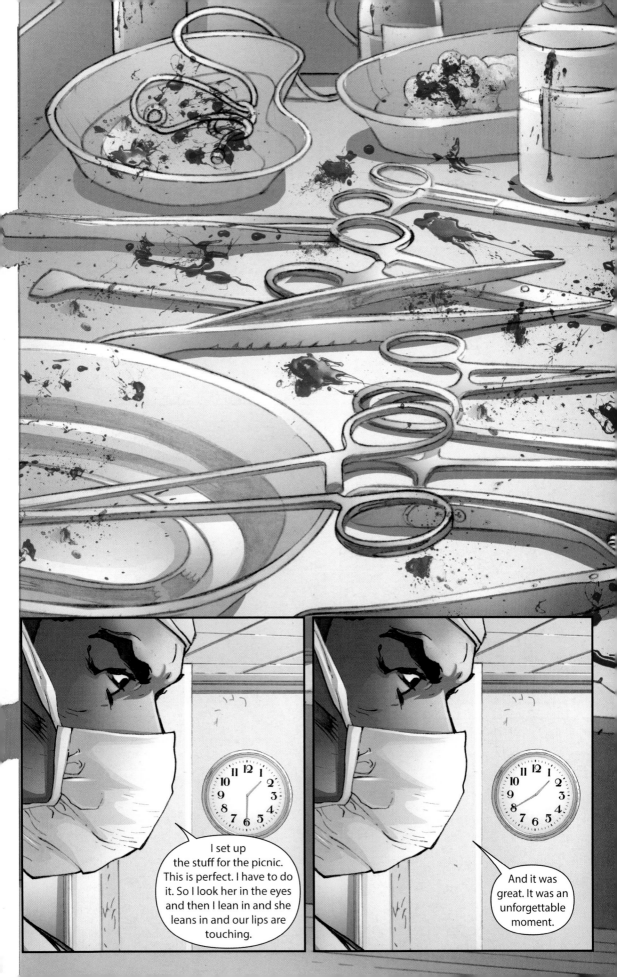

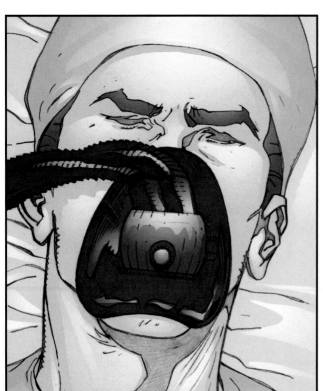

That was amazing, Doctor.

I had a great team.

Another "unforgettable moment?"

The thing about that? We started to walk back to her place and Angie says it's a shame she couldn't give me my surprise.

Do they know anything more about my husband?

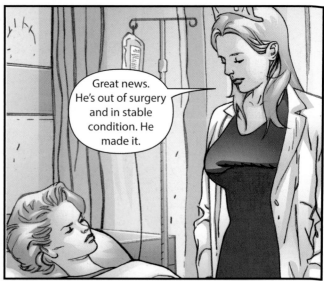

Great news. He's out of surgery and in stable condition. He made it.

Mrs. Stevens. I'm Dr. Bricker. I worked on your husband.

You were very lucky. Dr. Bricker went above and beyond. He saved your husband's life.

Super. Now can he save my f#ck#ng toe?

Or at least get me some new ice? It's starting to stink.

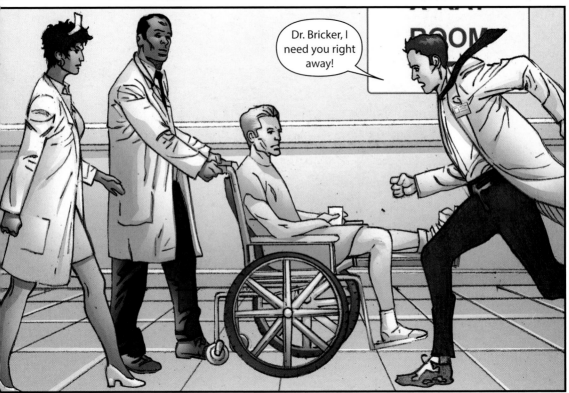

NEXT ISSUE

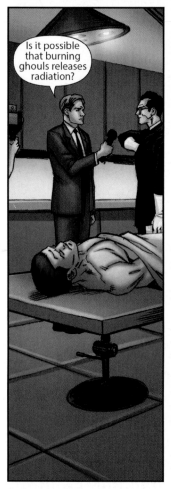

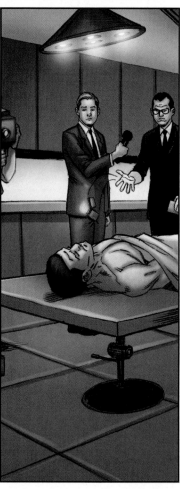

PREVIEW: **SLAB #1**

PREVIEW: **SLAB #1**

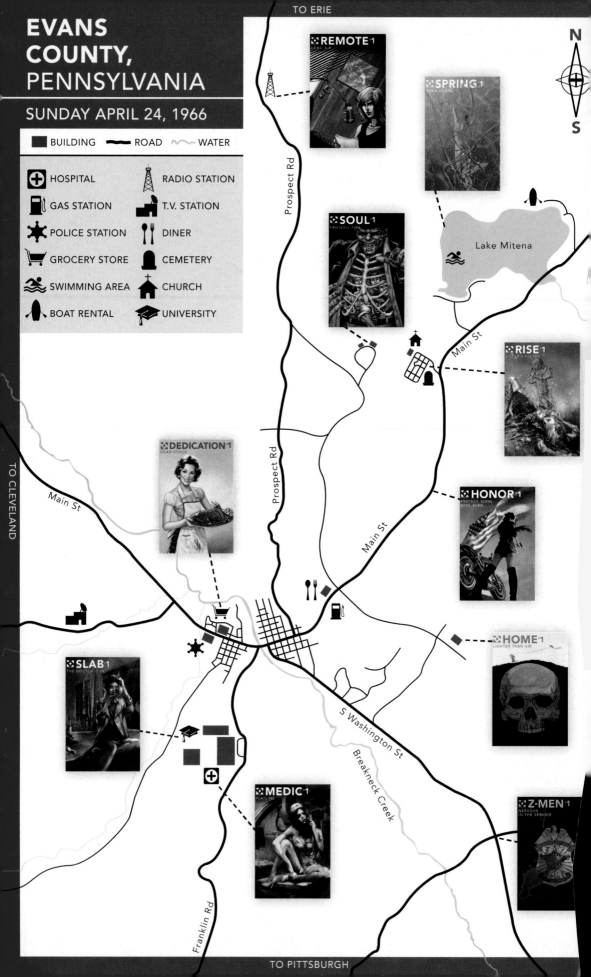